This book is dedicated to my family and all letter lovers.

www.mascotbooks.com

The Letter Critters Talent Show

Cover Design by Transcend Studio and Chase Taylor

For more information, please contact:
Mascot Books
620 Herndon Parkway, Suite 320
Herndon, VA 20170
info@mascotbooks.com

Library of Congress Control Number: 2020902780

CPSIA Code: PRT0320A
ISBN-13: 978-1-64543-448-1

Printed in the United States

THE LETTER CRITTERS
TALENT SHOW

WRITTEN AND ILLUSTRATED BY
CHASE TAYLOR

Today is the Letter Critters Talent
Show. All of the Critters in Letter Critter
Town are excited to perform today.

Letter Critter H goes up on stage
to host the show. He announces which
Letter Critters are going to share their talents.

Letter Critter **N** is the only one who does *not* participate in the talent show because he is very *negative.* No *need* to worry, he will change his mind.

The Vowelettes start
the show with their latest song
"A, E, I, O, U."

Letter Critter B blows beautiful bubbles of all her favorite shapes.

Letter Critter D does a drama where he is a doctor knight trying to rescue a damsel deer in distress.

Letter Critter F flies up
on stage dressed like a fairy.
She plays a fabulous tune
on her fancy flute.

Letter Critter G plays groovy tunes on his guitar.

Letter Critter **H** walks on
hot coals all the way off the stage.
Hopefully, he doesn't get **hurt**.

Letter Critter J performs her jumping jacks joyfully in a jumpsuit.

Letter Critter K kicks her kickball while Letter Critter C catches and throws it back to her.

Letter Critter **L** limbos
under a **log** pole. How **low** can he go?

Letter Critter **M** makes
his **most** favorite **meals** to
share with his friends after the show.

Letter Critter **N** now decides
to join the show. He **nibbles** all
his **nourishing noodles**
in under **nine** seconds.

Letter Critter P
paints pretty pictures.
His **personal** favorite
painting is a slice of *pizza*.

Letter Critter Q conducts
a quartet of quacking
ducks and quails.

Letter Critter R shows off
her most radical race track
she made for her racing cars. It
goes round and round.

Letter Critter S, the snake charmer, serenades snakes with a saxophone solo.

Letter Critter T does his most tremendous tap dance.

Letter Critter **V** does
ventriloquism with his
vulture dummy named **Val.**

Letter Critter **W** wows
the crowd **with** her **wonderful**
wig wardrobe.

Letter Critter **X** plays a **xylophone** while doing a handstand. She also takes **x-rays** of **boxes** to show what's inside them.

Letter Critter Y does
yoga while playing with a yellow
yo-yo tied to her toe.

Last but not least, Letter Critter
Z zips and zooms really fast
across the stage until he gets tired.
(He will get some ZZZZZs later.)

Letter Critter **H** returns to the stage
to announce the winner of the talent show.
Letter Critter **D** does a drum roll.

The winner of today's Talent Show is...
all of **The Letter Critters**
for making this such a fun day!

All **The Letter Critters** from **A-Z** showed they enjoyed the Talent Show with cheers and claps. **Letter Critter H** was congratulated for **hosting** the best Talent Show in The Letter Critter Town!

WHAT'S YOUR TALENT?

FUN FACTS ABOUT THE LETTER CRITTERS

- Half of the Letter Critters are boys, while the other half are girls.

- All the vowels are pink girls.

- Q has a huge crush on U.

- Whenever Y is used as a vowel, she turns pink.

- T is the only Letter Critter who wears shoes.

- J, Q, X, and Z are the rarest Letter Critters of the alphabet.

- Each Letter Critter tends to say words and phrases that start with their sound.

- All of the Letter Critters have lowercase red letters on their backs.

- The Letter Critters come in three different species: bears, fennec foxes, and squirrels.

The Letter Critters

THE LETTER CRITTERS' BIRTHDAYS

- A   April 8
- B   June 2
- C   December 12
- D   December 8
- E   April 11
- F   February 5
- G   September 20
- H   July 8
- I   May 18
- J   January 4
- K   October 14
- L   June 21
- M   May 2

- N   November 9
- O   October 1
- P   March 14
- Q   February 14
- R   August 3
- S   September 7
- T   January 10
- U   August 21
- V   June 20
- W   January 18
- X   February 29
- Y   November 25
- Z   December 31

ABOUT THE AUTHOR

Hello, my name is Chase. I created the adorable alphabet critters, The Letter Critters, when I was seventeen years old. I always loved letters and cute characters! My dream is to teach children the alphabet and new words in a fun way with my cute Letter Critters characters. The first book I wrote and illustrated is *The Letter Critters*. The second book is *The Letter Critters Biographies* book. *The Letter Critters Talent Show* is the third book of the Letter Critters series. My writing is from a young perspective, which will encourage children to learn.

Chase Taylor is a member of the National Honor Society, a Special Olympics Global Messenger and gold medalist, and the 2019 recipient of the Connecticut Arts Hero Award. In 2013, he starred in a Special Olympics Unified Sports™ softball commercial. Chase is the host of the cable and YouTube show, *The Social Chase*. Chase recently starred in an Autism Speaks national television Public Service Announcement for the "A Brighter Life on the Spectrum" Campaign.